Jan 19 –

Sweet Anne
All my love
Grandmother

A
FILLY
FOR
JOAN

By C. W. Anderson

A FILLY FOR JOAN

By C. W. Anderson

The Macmillan Company New York 1960

Library of Congress catalog card number: 60–12168

First Printing

The Macmillan Company, New York
Brett-Macmillan Ltd., Galt, Ontario

Printed in the United States of America

In memory of

Louis Albergini

1

Louis, huntsman of the Grafton Hounds, and idolized by the children to whom he taught riding, was jogging along a small wooded road on a big bay hunter. Beside him rode a little girl on a piebald pony. Her dark hair bobbed in rhythm as she posted to the quick trot. Her clear dark eyes were intent as she listened to Louis. This lean, weather-beaten huntsman had been around horses all his life and had an endless fund of stories and information about them. In Joan he had the perfect audience, for she loved horses—talked of them in her waking hours and dreamed of them in her sleep. Her greatest desire was to be a good rider and eventually to have a horse of her own. When Louis talked, she listened eagerly and stored away everything he said. She felt sure that he knew more about horses than anybody in the world.

"Some people think of a horse as a stupid animal," said Louis, "but if you are around them long enough you'll see that they are just like people. Some are quick to learn, some backward, some are kind and obedient, some are stubborn. And it's not all their fault. Almost everything a horse is he inherits from his sire and dam. When you see a horse that's tough and stubborn you can be pretty sure either his father or mother were like that—maybe both. And when you see one with a perfect disposition—one that always tries to do the right thing—you know someone took care to mate a sweet-dispositioned mare to a well-mannered stallion.

The saying 'Blood will tell' isn't always true with people but with horses you can almost bet on it—especially when it comes to disposition."

He paused for a moment and then went on; "Many people talk only of size and bone and conformation when buying a horse. When I want to know what a man is like I don't ask how tall he is or what he weighs or how broad his shoulders are. I want

to know if he's kind and honest. Man or horse, that's what's important. One of the handsomest horses I ever laid hands on I wouldn't take as a gift. He was tricky and undependable, just like a dishonest man. You could never tell what he was going to do except that it wouldn't be good. Then there was old Granite. You'd never look at him twice, he was so plain—unless you noticed his eye. Then you knew you could trust him anywhere, anytime. Though he didn't have that Thoroughbred look, he was a gentleman through and through. What he had he gave even before you asked for it."

"But where would you find one like that, Louis? My mother says I can have a horse of my own when I'm sixteen, but where would we ever find a horse like that? Nobody who owned such a horse would want to sell him."

"I wouldn't try to find him. Anytime you see a horse for sale you can be pretty sure there's something wrong with him. And if it's manners and disposition, it's bred in him and nobody is apt to get it out. So why not start from the beginning and breed your own horse? Choose the disposition you want in the mare and the stallion and then you'll know what you are getting. It would take time, but it's worth waiting for."

"But Louis, would you be sure the colt would turn out just right?"

"Not dead sure," he said, "but sure enough so I'd bet on it. Maybe the colt won't have the same conformation, but if his sire and dam both had good dispositions you can be pretty sure he'll be a nice, kind colt. That almost always comes through."

Louis flicked a fly from his horse's neck with his crop and went on; "I've often thought of breeding a horse especially for one person—just suited to that person. If it's for a bold rider I'd plan it differently. A bold rider would spoil a gentle horse; a timid rider would be ruined by a strong, bold horse. The horse and rider have to fit if there's to be any pleasure in it."

"If you were going to breed one for me what would it be like?" asked Joan.

Louis looked down at the earnest little rider and noted how carefully she remembered all his instructions. The heels were down, the seat erect and easy and the hands light on the reins.

"I'd try for a gentle, sensitive horse with a bold streak just underneath," he said smiling.

Joan was quiet for a long time. Then she said, "Why don't you try it sometime, Louis? Wouldn't Ladybird get a wonderful colt? She's the nicest horse I know."

"She would," said Louis. "I think she will."

"You've already done it!" cried Joan.

"Yes," said Louis. "A lady heard me speak of my idea, and she wants a colt for her little girl. Then they can grow up together and know each other from the start. By the time the colt is old enough to be ridden, they'll be a real team. Especially since they'll be alike. At least I hope so," he added under his breath.

"Oh, Louis! What a lucky girl. Who is she?"

"I'm not sure I remember," said Louis with a trace of a smile, "but it seems to me her name was Joan."

5

2

LADYBIRD received more attention that summer than ever before. Joan often came over to the stable just to be around the lovely mare that was to present her with a colt of her very own. She never ceased to marvel at the velvety softness of Ladybird's muzzle when she searched her for the tidbit she knew would be there.

"If my colt will be like you that's all I ask," said Joan softly as she stroked the dark, satiny neck. "Just as gentle and nice, and a good jumper." The mare rubbed her head gently against Joan's arm.

Louis saw Joan in the paddock and strolled over to her.

"What do you want your foal to be," he asked, "a colt or a filly?"

"Oh, I hope it's a filly so it will grow up to be just like Ladybird. I think she is the loveliest horse there ever was."

"She's nice," said Louis. "She's about as nice as they come. And she's just as good as she is nice. Did you ever see what she won? Come and I'll show you."

"Did she win all those?" cried Joan. An entire wall of the tack room was covered with ribbons, most of them blue. There were half a dozen with long ribbon streamers that Joan knew stood for championships.

"Nobody was beating her when she was right," said Louis. "I remember when she won that one," pointing to one of the championship ribbons. "My car broke down on the way to the

6

show. I was bringing Ladybird in a small trailer. We were hung up for hours before we could get under way. When we finally got to the show there were only three hunter classes left. The way the points stood she would have to win them all to have a chance at the championship. She went like a dream and won the first two classes in style—and she had to beat some good horses to do it. The last class was the toughest. That outside course was rugged but three horses had good clean rounds. The one we had to beat couldn't be faulted. To beat a hundred per cent performance was really a job. Finally our turn came. She went beautifully; perfect pace, standing back from her fences and jumping them big and in stride. As we came over the in and out I realized we'd have to show the judges something extra. I dropped the reins on her neck and let her do the rest all on her own. She took those last two fences right through the middle, looking neither left nor right. The crowd gave her a terrific hand. Of course some said I was showing off. But I felt I had to let the judges see what an honest mare she was. She knew what was expected of her, and she didn't need a rider. There aren't many like that."

Joan's eyes were shining. "That was wonderful," she cried. "She won didn't she? She'd have to win after that."

"Yes, she won the class and the championship, but it was her last show. She came up lame and it never quite cleared up. She was all right for easy hacking but that leg never was up to jumping again. I think she misses it a lot, too. It's in her blood. I see her eyeing these fences sometimes, sort of measuring them the way she used to. When the grass is especially rich and green out

7

in that field beyond her paddock I wonder if she'll sail over. But she never does. She's a Lady."

"Was she a fine jumper right from the start or did you have to school her?" asked Joan.

"Even as a foal she was a natural jumper," said Louis. "Time and again I've seen her take this paddock fence. She'd always come back to her mother again but she loved to jump. And her form was just as good then as when she was a champion. It was born in her."

"Do you think my filly will be like that?" asked Joan. "Oh, I hope she will."

"So you're sure it's going to be a filly," said Louis with a smile. "Well, you may be right. It always seems to me that a mare is gentler with a filly than with a colt. Sometimes I even think I see it in their eyes when they're carrying the foal. Look at Ladybird! Did you ever see a gentler look in a horse's eye?"

Joan stroked the mare's dark head. "She's the loveliest thing ever," she said, "just perfect." She was silent for a moment. "You think my filly will really be like her?"

"I wouldn't dare to say that she will be as good a jumper. You never can tell how much of that comes through," answered Louis. "But in disposition—you can be almost certain of that. And even if she's only half as good as Ladybird she'd still be a good horse. Yes, a real good horse." A faraway look came into his eyes.

"Do you know what she did for me once? I was broke and needed some money badly. I was barely able to scrape up the entry fee for this Fairfield show. She won each class we went in,

8

but neither of us could eat silk ribbons, and her oat bin was about as empty as my kitchen shelves. Then I noticed that the open jumper class had a five-hundred-dollar cash prize. I used my last five dollars for the entry fee. She'd never jumped in the ring in that sort of class—she liked to jump with speed and gallop along between her fences with a long, reaching stride. These big jumps so close together were tricky, and Lord only knows how high they would put them if the competition got tough. And it was pretty sure to be, for there were some top open jumpers entered. So all I could do was hope and pray.

"It was a 'knock down and out' class and they started it at three feet six. That only eliminated a few horses that had no business there in the first place. But there was a big bay and a gray that really knew their business, and I saw we'd have our work cut out for us.

"At four feet a lot of them began knocking off bars, so when they raised the height again there were only five of us left. Ladybird had really surprised me the way she took to this new game. Many a good hunter that is brilliant on an outside course is no good at all in the ring. A horse has to be handy and quick as a cat to come into these jumps right with just a few strides between fences. More than that, they have to have a real 'lep' in them, as the Irish say. Any decent hunter can jump a four-foot fence when they have a run at it but notice how many make mistakes at the in and outs. An 'open horse' can't rely on speed. He's got to be able to put in a short stride if he comes into a fence wrong, and jump from almost a standstill. His hind quarters have to be like steel springs.

9

And without schooling that's what Ladybird showed me that day."

Louis ran his hand over the mare's sloping shoulder. "That's where her smooth gallop comes from," he said, "but it's back here that the jump is. Do you know she was almost muscled like this when she was six weeks old?" He passed his hand over her powerful, sleek quarters. "Do you see that deep crease? When you see that, you know there is power under it. Many foals don't get it until they're weanlings. That little filly had it almost from the start. Every muscle was chiseled sharp and clear. The first time I looked at her a funny feeling, almost like a shiver, ran up my back. I felt this was something special."

He looked affectionately at the dark eye that watched him so knowingly. "Well, after four feet there were only three of us left; Ladybird, the bay and the gray. At four feet six the other two touched a few bars but not enough to knock them off. Ladybird still went clean, never touched a fence. And she did it so gaily and gracefully that the crowd loved her. When the judges called to raise the bars to five feet I knew we were really up against something.

"Horses that can really jump five feet are few and far between," continued Louis. "I hear people tell of this tremendous fence they jumped, more than five feet; but you get a yardstick and measure, and it's apt to turn out to be four feet rather than five. A fence always looks big from the top of a horse and even bigger once you're over it. But when you face a five-foot jump in the ring it's all there and looks as big as a house.

"The bay ticked a few of the rails lightly but went well until

he came in wrong at the eighth. He sent the rails flying on that one. Still it might have been good enough to win, for I couldn't see either the gray or my mare going clean over those twelve huge fences. Then came the gray's turn, and as he took the first few fences, my heart sank. Man, he could jump! Fence after fence and nothing but the slightest tick at any of them. He came into the last one a little too fast and took off too close in. There just wasn't room to get up high enough and he sent the top bar sailing."

"Oh Louis! That meant Ladybird had to have a perfect round, didn't it?" cried Joan. "Did she? Tell me quickly if she did."

Louis smiled down at the eager, flushed face. "You like the happy ending, don't you? So do I. Those are the ones that a horseman always tells. Those are the ones he likes to remember.

"I patted her neck and turned her to the first fence. I decided to let her choose her own pace; do it her own way. I was afraid I'd start thinking of how much we needed that money and maybe try too hard. That's often a good way to mess things up. But I needn't have worried. She is every inch a Thoroughbred with heart enough for two. I never in my life saw a horse measure her fences like she did that day. Her jump was without a fault and you never heard such cheering. When I felt that powerful thrust of her quarters I knew we were in."

Joan's eyes were glowing. She turned and put her arms around Ladybird's neck and hugged her hard. "You're wonderful, just wonderful," she said.

"They paid the prize money in gold," said Louis. "The first gold I'd ever had. Man, did I feel good as we rode back to the

12

van with all that gold jingling in my pocket. Now I felt my luck had turned. We would eat, and well, and everything seemed right with the world. Do you know the first thing I bought with our winnings? I stopped at a fruit stand and bought a bushel of carrots and a bushel of apples. Ladybird loved carrots and apples and that night she had a feast. Not all of that, of course, but plenty. And do you know I'm sure she knew what it was for. She knew she'd done well and that I was trying to thank her."

3

"You're doing well," said Louis as he watched Joan holding her pony to a slow canter with a light hand on the reins. "Tomorrow we'll put you on Ladybird. You're too big for that pony, and I want you to get the feel of a real horse."

"Oh I'd love that, Louis, but do you think I can handle her right? She's such a wonderful horse, and I don't want to spoil her."

"You'll never spoil her," said Louis. "You have light, sensitive hands and you never get nervous. It's the nervous rider more than the rough one that spoils a horse's mouth. He's always afraid something is going to happen and keeps tightening up on the reins. If the horse is doing nothing wrong he resents it all the more because he knows he doesn't deserve it. A horse knows when he's doing wrong just as a disobedient child does, and he doesn't resent being punished at such times. In some ways he has just as much of a sense of fairness as a person."

He paused a moment and then said, "You don't remember Chieftan, do you? No, that must have been ten years ago or more. He was a big red chestnut, high-headed, with a lot of fire in his eye. I always suspected there was Man o' War blood there, although I never had his papers. But he was a Thoroughbred; it was written all over him. One of grandest horses I ever sat on and I not only got him for nothing, they paid me to cart him away."

Here was another of Louis' wonderful stories. Joan was excited.

14

No one could tell a story like Louis. "Oh please tell me about him, Louis. He sounds like a wonderful horse. How did you get him for nothing?"

"Well, I got a call one morning to come over to this man's place and pick up a horse he wanted destroyed. He said he would pay me twenty dollars to cart him away. I'd seen this man out hunting and I never liked the way he handled a horse. He was big, rough and loud; just the kind a horse hates. He had a lot of money and a big stable of expensive hunters but under him they all looked nervous, almost wild-eyed. You could see that they never knew when he'd be after them with spurs or whip or bit. Many of those horses looked like they'd go perfectly in a snaffle but he always had a tough bit on them and a choking hold on the reins. So I had a doubt in my mind as I drove over with my light van."

He turned to her and said, "Did you ever see a horse that was a killer? That was what they let out of the stable. The groom was scared to death of the horse. He had him on a long line with a pitchfork in his hand to keep him at a distance. I saw we would never load him in a hundred years the way he was. You could see he hated both the groom and the owner, who kept at a good distance. I didn't like the looks of the job but I thought of the old saying, 'A true horseman must know neither fear nor anger.' I try to live by that."

Joan remembered seeing Louis drive over all but impossible fences to be with his hounds and she knew how well he lived by it. Her mother had once read a hunting poem of Masefield's to her and the description of the huntsman was, to her, Louis, and no one

else. "And a courage terrible to see." It made a shiver run up her spine. That was Louis, although so quiet and gentle.

"They told me this horse had become so savage that after he bucked off his rider he tried his best to trample him to death. Soon no one even dared to come near him. But when I looked at him I couldn't see real viciousness in him. He had the look of a high-spirited horse that had been mistreated to a point that drove him almost mad. He'd had all he could take, and now that he had discovered his power he wouldn't take any more."

Louis smiled at the remembrance. "That was an afternoon. First I took the horse and made the owner and groom get out of sight. It was clear that the horse hated them, and I could never do anything with him when they were there. I led him around and talked to him quietly. Soon I noticed he kept looking at me with almost a surprised look in his eye. I don't suppose he'd heard anyone speak gently to him since he came to that stable. I knew I had to wipe a lot of things out of his mind if he was ever going to get into that van with me so I took my time. The best way to get nowhere with a nervous horse is to hurry him. I let him graze along the road where there was nice high grass and I kept talking to him. Did you ever notice how a horse or dog likes to hear your voice if you make it soft and kind? You can do a lot with your voice; more than most people ever realize.

"Well, after an hour or so the big horse seemed quieter. I kept looking him over and I still couldn't see any sign of viciousness in him. It only showed when the owner or groom were in sight. What they had done to him I couldn't imagine, but it must have been plenty. Finally I put out my hand slowly and patted his neck. Again I got that surprised look. Then he let me touch his head. As I stroked it gently, still talking to him, I saw the ears come forward and the white of the eye disappear. When I led him to the van he hesitated a moment, looking around, and then, as if he decided any place would be better than this, he walked quietly up the ramp."

"That poor horse must have been terribly abused, Louis!" exclaimed Joan. "I'll bet he changed a lot after you had him."

"I kept him around the place for several weeks just letting him relax and forget the past. Maybe under bad treatment he had become an outlaw and would always be a vicious bucker. I'd have to find out sooner or later but I wasn't in any hurry. That fellow had power, and a look in his eye that made you feel no one was going to ride him if he had other ideas. I wanted everything in my favor before I tackled him.

"One day I had him turned out in a big paddock when I let out some of the hounds for a little exercise. They made for the paddock and began running and playing around him. They were racing down the paddock together when I saw something I would never believe if I hadn't seen it. One of the hounds was running in front of him right under his feet. I was sure he'd be trampled. But the big horse pulled up that fore leg and continued on three legs for half a dozen strides until the hound was in the clear. He almost went down but he was not going to trample the hound! It was clear that he loved hounds. If I could ride him I knew I had a real hunter."

18

"That was wonderful!" cried Joan. "How I would have loved that horse! Did he become a fine hunter, Louis?"

"I rode him the next day and he was perfect. A lot of horse, you understand, but not a mean thing about him. Then I hunted hounds on him and he was the grandest hunter you ever saw. He would do anything to be with hounds. He never thought of a fence no matter how big it was; his heart was with the hounds in the field beyond, and he would have jumped over a house to get with them. One day I was schooling a green horse over the jumps when he came into one wrong and we had a smashing fall. It knocked me out, and when I came to I found I was almost deaf. The doctor said it would clear up but I was worried. How would I be able to hunt hounds? You know in this wooded country where hounds are often following the fox's line through woods too thick to ride through you have to depend on your ears as much as your eyes to know which way to go. But I needn't have worried. Chieftan did it all for me. He was a better huntsman than I. All I had to do was watch his ears and I'd know where hounds were. For three weeks he really hunted the pack. I just went along for the ride. And to think this was a horse I was supposed to destroy as an outlaw! You know there is an old English saying, 'Show me your horse, and I will tell you what you are.' That's one of the truest things I ever heard."

4

"How WOULD you like to change back to your pony?" asked Louis as he watched Joan posting to the swinging trot of the sleek bay mare.

"Never in the world!" exclaimed Joan fervently. "He's all right for children but once I've ridden Ladybird I could never think of a pony again. Just to sit on her when she walks is a dream, and her trot . . ." Words failed her, but Louis, looking at her shining face, understood.

"Many people like riding but only a few get all the pleasure that there is in riding a fine horse. You have to love horses, and you must also try to perfect your riding. So many are satisfied if they can just stick on a horse. That's like being satisfied with playing the piano with one finger. To be a fine rider you must understand horses thoroughly. You must understand what they think. An experienced horseman knows just what a horse will do, what will frighten him or make him nervous. An unexpected shy can throw an unsuspecting rider; many get hurt that way. I once knew a horse that was such a terrific shier that his owner finally gave him away. And he'd paid fifteen hundred dollars for him!"

"Couldn't he be cured at all, Louis?"

"Well I can't quite say I cured him. I helped him some and he helped me a lot. After I had him I never rode slack or careless on any horse. He could really shy. He'd drop from under you, and

21

you'd think he was falling; but he just spread his legs wide, and
then he'd go about six feet to the side in a leap that was like
lightning. If you weren't riding a close seat with a good knee grip
you were gone. He'd thrown his owner and everyone else that
tried to ride him so often that they finally gave up and no one
wanted him.

"If he hadn't been such a grand-looking horse I wouldn't have
taken him, even as a gift. What could I do with him? I couldn't

put anyone I was teaching on him and I couldn't use him myself, for teaching. A shy could unsettle a quiet horse.

"And you could just imagine my trying to hunt hounds with him. I had plenty of horses to feed already, but there was something about him that got me. He was proud and high-headed with a wonderful sloping shoulder. It was a pleasure just to look at him. I've had a lot of horses in my day but do you know I still remember that wonderful top line of his. It flowed from his ear over a beautifully set wither, through a short back, with just enough room for a saddle. His quarters were perfect. I thought even if I couldn't do anything with him just to have a horse like that around to look at everyday would make you feel good. He was everything a horseman dreams of except maybe the eye. It was a quick, knowing eye with a glint in it. And the ears were very alert and always moving. I said to myself, 'This horse sees too much.' "

"What do you mean, Louis? I thought it was good for a horse to have keen eyes."

"A horse can be a shier because his eyesight is poor; he doesn't see things until they are on top of him. But if a horse has too quick an eye, he's apt to be startled because he gets a quick glimpse of something far away. He never gets the whole story until it's too late. A big powerful horse would not be apt to be afraid of a bird or squirrel or rabbit if he saw it full and clear, but when he sees a flash of something moving suddenly, it's different. And this fellow, Pawnee, had another angle that helped explain everything. He'd been raised in the west—Wyoming I think it was. That didn't mean anything to me at first except to be surprised he'd

23

been broken gentle instead of cowboy fashion. The first time I sat on him I could tell no spur had ever touched this horse. It would be like trying to put out a fire with gasoline."

"What did his being raised in the west have to do with his shying, Louis?"

"Well, I was riding him one day, along a hard road and a dried leaf blew across the road making a rattling sound. Pawnee dropped and gave a sideways leap that took us clear into the ditch. I found myself halfway up his neck. If he had given another jump I would have been off, but he let me get back into the saddle and find my stirrups. I'd ridden many horses that shied but nothing like that. It was chained lightning. But I realized it wasn't a trick—all he would have had to do was to give an extra buck and he would have gotten rid of me if that's what he wanted. No, he was really frightened. And suddenly I knew why.

"Heels out a little more," said Louis looking over at Joan. "Don't grip with the lower part of your leg. Keep the grip in the thigh and the knee."

"I'm sorry, Louis. I'll remember. Why did a dry leaf frighten him so?"

"I kept thinking about it. That was the most terrific shy he ever showed me and I knew he was frightened. Then it came to me. I spent a summer out west when I was a youngster, and one day after I came back I remember jumping almost out of my skin at the sound of a dry leaf blowing over the sidewalk. It was exactly the sound that a rattlesnake makes when he is about to strike! And a horse is deathly afraid of snakes. He'd probably seen

plenty of them and when he heard that rattle he was taking no chances. Then I began to get the whole picture. Out west everything was in the open and clear to see. Outside of snakes almost anything that moved would be seen a long distance away. Nothing appeared suddenly and unexpectedly. Then he was brought back here where the country is all enclosed. His eyes had been trained by those long distances to notice things as sharply as a western pony or an Indian. Here he saw too much, too suddenly. He hadn't gotten used to it—probably never would. At least that's the way it looked to me."

"What did you do with him then? I know you tried to cure him but how did you go about it?"

"First I put him in a box stall that had windows on two sides and I cleaned those windows thoroughly. One looked out on a road where quite a bit of traffic went by. I wanted him to see everything. I'd found out that the stall he'd had was dark; no window, and there was no paddock. And he was as tight as a violin string; you could feel it when you got into the saddle; think what that must have done to him. It wouldn't be good for any horse. But for him, raised as he was, it was much worse."

"The poor horse!" exclaimed Joan. "He must have been happy in that new stall."

"He was and you should have seen him in that big paddock. He'd go around it with his head in the air, his nostrils flaring, carrying his tail like a flag. He was really something to see."

"How was he for riding? Was he better about shying?" asked Joan.

"He improved but when something startled him, he still put in a terrific one. It would have put most riders down. I tried to keep my eyes open to see things as quickly as he did so I'd be ready for his shy, but that was hard to do. He had the eye of a hawk, and when he let go, it was like a steel spring uncoiled. But you couldn't get mad at him. He couldn't help it."

Louis paused a moment. "He did something once that I'd never seen before and never expect to see again. We were riding along this road, and a partridge went up just in front of us. You know how they can explode and really startle you. Pawnee almost came apart. His shy was so violent that he went to his knees when he landed. Anytime a horse goes to his knees you can be pretty sure he's going down. But not that horse. He went along on his knees for half a dozen strides and came up again! I don't know how he did it. It must have been his pride. He was the proudest horse I've ever known. I don't believe he'd ever been down, and he wasn't going to begin then."

"You must have loved that horse, Louis. Whatever became of him?"

"Well, I couldn't put anybody on him; it was too risky. I'd get up an hour early just to get him out. Lord knows I had plenty of horses that had to be exercised, but there was something about this horse that made riding seem all new again. He was really a person. There was a young boy who had begun riding at the stable. He hadn't had much training, but he was mad about horses and learned quickly. I noticed when he paid me for his ride some of the money would be quarters and dimes. I knew, the way he felt about horses, he would be riding much oftener if he could afford it. So I offered him the chance to exercise some of the horses. You should have seen his face light up."

"Oh Louis, that was a nice thing to do."

"It worked out well for me, too. He was a natural with horses. He learned more in two months than many riders do in two years. But one thing I noticed; he couldn't stay away from Pawnee. He liked all the horses, but he always lingered longest at Pawnee's stall. And the horse seemed to like him. I knew he was dying to ride the horse but I wasn't sure how it would work out. Finally one day I told him he could take Pawnee out. I still remember the look on his face. I don't know if he even heard me when I warned him about his shying. He just stood looking at the horse as if it were Man o' War himself.

"They were gone a long time, and I'd begun to worry when I saw them coming down the road. The boy had Pawnee on a loose rein and the horse was trotting as gaily as I'd ever seen him. I didn't need to ask how they'd gotten along. The way the horse rubbed his head against the boy's shoulder told the story. When I saw that he had brought the horse in nice and quiet and not a wet hair on him, I said he could ride Pawnee whenever he wanted to. Often he was over at daybreak to get a ride before school or work that had to be done. The more I saw of them the more I realized that boy and horse belonged together. I kept turning things over in my mind, and one day I drove over to his place. They had a small farm near Lynford, well kept, mostly garden stuff. I found the boy out at the stable. He was just finishing a box

28

stall. It was made of old lumber but it was a fine job. Everything was there, feed box, rack for water bucket, bracket for salt block and two good windows.

" 'I didn't know you were getting a horse,' I said.

"He looked a little flustered. 'Maybe some day,' he said. 'But I had to have a stable first. Now I'll start to save up for a horse.' "

"Oh, I hope he got his horse," cried Joan.

"He did," said Louis. "I rode over before dawn leading Pawnee and put him in the stall without anyone seeing me. I'd liked to have seen that boy's face when he came down to the stable."

Joan looked at Louis earnestly. "Oh, Louis," she said, "you are such a nice man."

5

FOR JOAN the days went slowly. Her mind was constantly on the little filly that would arrive in the spring—in early April, Louis thought. Her mother had told her that this was her birthday present. Wouldn't it be wonderful if the filly would arrive in time for her birthday? She always thought of it as a filly. Of course she would be happy if it was a colt but she felt sure it was going to be a filly. And she felt certain that the little filly would grow up to be like Ladybird. In her eyes, Ladybird was perfection itself.

The winter had been severe so there was little riding, and when March came with thaws and milder days Ladybird was big with foal. Joan changed to another horse in the stable, a handsome chestnut with a white blaze. Riding was as much a part of her life as eating and sleeping. She could not do without it. Now she was beginning to learn how much horses differed from each other and that in each you can find some trait or characteristic that made them interesting. None of them was Ladybird, of course, but Golden Boy had a lovely slow canter, and he would go on forever without urging. He never needed another horse beside him, to make him go willingly; in fact he seemed to like to go out alone. She recalled how impossible her pony was unless there was another horse with him, constantly trying to turn back to the stable. She remembered Louis having told her that George Washington, who was a fine horseman, said that the one thing he required of a horse was that "he would go along." Feeling this willingness of spirit beneath her, she knew now what he meant. She patted the golden neck and said, "You're a fine horse. George Washington would have liked you."

When they got back to the stable Louis noticed how pleased she looked. "Ladybird had better hurry along with her colt or she won't be tops with you," he said.

"Oh no, Louis. She'll always be my very favorite but Golden Boy is wonderful too. Isn't his canter lovely?"

"I suppose you had to use your crop a lot," said Louis with a smile. "This old lazybones needed a good deal of stirring up didn't he?" He patted the chestnut horse fondly.

"Louis, are there many horses like him—so willing to go when they're out alone?"

"The only other one I know of is Ladybird. And even she is happier if there is another horse with her. Horses love each other's company. Did you ever notice when they're out grazing how they'll always be right together no matter how large their paddock is? That is, all but Golden Boy. He's sort of a lone wolf—likes to be by himself. You'll never see him join any of the horse play that goes on in the paddock. If he pays any attention at all, it will be only to look sort of bored with such foolishness."

"I've noticed that, Louis. What makes him like that?"

"Well, it may be because he was an orphan. His mother died giving birth to him. I didn't have a mare that could nurse him so I raised him on a bottle. I didn't have to use the bottle very long; he soon learned to drink out of a pail. It was then that I first noticed his manners. No matter how hungry he was he never pushed around or spilled anything. He had real manners. Maybe that was why the other colts picked on him. They made life miserable for him so I finally put him in a paddock by himself. That suited him fine. He never looked for companionship except maybe from me. All I had to do was to stand at the fence and he would come trotting over."

"He still does that, Louis. I've seen him. He certainly likes you."

Louis patted the smooth neck of the big chestnut. "He's a real gentleman. I've never seen him do a wrong thing. You know he was really the one who gave me the idea of breeding a horse especially for one person. Both his sire and dam had unusually

32

good dispositions and manners. That all came through. He's not a great jumper, and he hasn't a lot of speed; but what he has you can call on any time, and it will all be there. That's what I want in a horse. All the fine conformation in the world isn't worth anything without it."

"Have you ever shown him, Louis? I should think he would be wonderful over an outside course."

"I had him in a few shows, and he won his share, but I could see he didn't care for it. He's a very intelligent horse, and he wants to have a reason for doing things. Out hunting he knows he's got to get over fences to be with hounds. But I could see that going over the same fences on the same course didn't appeal to him. Many fine hunters turn sour if they're campaigned too long at the shows. With his disposition he would probably never do that, but he might become bored and lose that springy willingness that makes it such a pleasure to ride him."

"I know what you mean, Louis. Since I quit riding ponies and rode Ladybird and Golden Boy it's all so different. They want to go, and you feel they enjoy it as much as you do."

Louis smiled to himself and shook his head. "Lord only knows how many horses I've ridden, good, bad, and indifferent; but when I get on a good horse I feel just as I did when I started. I've tried to explain that to people who don't ride, but they can't understand it. When riding has been your job for thirty years they think you'd be fed up with it. But they don't realize the companionship there is between yourself and a good horse if you really understand each other."

6

JOAN WAS just coming down the stairs for breakfast when the phone rang. When she answered it she recognized Louis' voice. "Happy Birthday!" he said. "There's a birthday present for you here. Just came an hour or two ago."

"Oh, Louis, it's not——!"

"Yes, it's a filly. And a very nice filly. She's already up on her feet nursing. And she looks like Ladybird even now." He waited a moment but heard nothing. "Hello!" he called.

"Oh wonderful! A filly, and on my birthday! I'm so happy. I'll be right over!"

The dark little foal stood pressed against Ladybird's side looking at Joan with wide, questioning eyes. Already she knew that the gentle man who had helped her to her feet so she could have her mother's good milk was a friend, and she felt that the girl who looked at her now with such big, shining eyes also liked her. Ladybird nuzzled Louis and Joan gently, and the little filly no longer felt any fear in her new surroundings.

"Louis, she does look like Ladybird," said Joan softly. She felt like whispering in the presence of the soft, downy, long-legged youngster that seemed almost more like a fawn than a horse. "Around the head, I mean, and her eyes. It's the same expression —so gentle."

35

"You're going to have a good eye for a horse," said Louis looking down at her. "That's what I was breeding for—what's in the head. And I think it's there. I see it and so do you. If we get that, don't worry about the rest. I already see good points in her body and her legs are very straight for a newborn foal."

"I never realized how long a young foal's legs are, Louis. I never saw one so young before. Is that the way they should be?"

Louis laughed. "It always surprises you. It's strange that the legs should be so out-of-proportion to the rest of the body but that's the way it always is. There is an old saying that a foal's legs are as long at birth as they will ever be. It's not true but you can see why someone thought so."

"She's just a darling, Louis. I'd like to hug her but I won't. I can see she's shy and timid yet. I'll just look at her for a while."

Louis looked down at her approvingly. "That's best. Wait till she comes to you. And the one thing that will win her confidence it gentleness. That and a soft, kind voice count for more than all the training advice I could ever give you."

"What was her sire like, Louis? I don't even know his name."

"He was as well-bred a stallion as you'll find anywhere. His name was Bright Armour and he was by Gallant Knight who was a great race horse. He inherited his sire's fine disposition but not his speed. If he had, I could never have afforded to breed to him. But he had enough to win races—not the big stakes but allowance races and he was always doing his best. I used to see him at the track and I always had a little bet on him when he ran. I got a thrill out of seeing him come along in the stretch from way back

and get up in the last stride to get his head in front. He was always outrun the first part of the race, but he had enough heart to make up for his lack of speed."

"I'm glad you told me about him, Louis. Now I feel I know him, and I'm proud he's the sire of my filly."

"Remember, when I'm speaking of lack of speed I'm speaking of racing. A fourth-class race horse would have plenty of speed to be a hunter, and he was a lot better than that. So for what we wanted he had everything." He was thoughtful for a moment; "Breeding is a funny thing," he said. "Sometimes quality will skip a generation or even two and then show up again. If it's in the blood it can come out, and Bright Armour has the blood of a champion. There was a horse by the great Bull Lea out of a fine mare who should have been a world-beater, and he turned out to be nothing. One small race out of twelve starts was the best he could do. He had all the looks of his sire and dam but none of their ability. Still with those fine blood lines a small breeder gave him a chance at stud. His first five colts were nothing to speak of and then came Black Shield. He was a throwback to his grandsire and grandam, and was one of the best horses of his day. If there's fine blood in him, there's always a chance a stallion may outbreed himself." He studied the little filly carefully.

"Yes, there's always a chance," he added, almost to himself.

7

"Louis, isn't she growing fast. I think I can see a difference every day." Joan was stroking the head of the little filly as she looked up at Joan trustingly. It hadn't taken long for this youngster to learn that everyone loved her.

Louis nodded and then said, "She's looking more like Ladybird every day. Around the head, I mean. In her body I see a lot of her sire, Bright Armour. She's going to be more rugged than Ladybird. She has more bone than most foals her age. See how strong she is below the knee and hock."

"But I thought Ladybird was perfect, Louis."

"She comes closer than most, but you must remember the leg that gave way under jumping. She was a little too fine in the legs, too delicate. That's where the trouble almost always comes. I'm glad your filly is going to be more rugged."

He studied the little filly intently. "Watching a foal grow and develop is one of the most interesting things I know of. A little at a time you see its breeding come through; something of the sire, something of the dam. Do you see how high your filly carries her head? That goes back five generations to the great Man o' War. You've got his blood there, you know. He always carried a high, proud head and most of his offspring are the same. Some horsemen consider that a fault but when they run like he did, and like so many of his sons and daughters did, you can't call it

40

a fault." The faraway look that Joan knew so well came into his eye. "No sir," he said softly, "you can't call it a fault."

"Oh tell me about it, Louis. I know it's something exciting. I love your stories."

"It isn't really a story. It's just something that happened at the race track years ago. You know I was with race horses before I came to hunting, and I still like to go to the track. It's the horses I go for, not the betting. Oh, once in a while I make a small bet, but it's more to back a horse I like than any idea of making money. But once it worked both ways," he smiled at the recollection. "That was a day; that really was a day," he said.

"There was a man who had a lovely filly that I wanted in the worst way. He had set a high price on her, and he refused any kind of a trade that I could make. I'd tried again that morning and he turned me down cold. I felt pretty low as I sat reading my paper. Then I saw that Stymie was running in the Massachusetts Handicap that afternoon. There was a horse I was crazy about. He had come up from nothing at all; running in the cheapest races and not winning often then. But as he got older he began to find himself. There was good blood; he had the Man o' War strain in both sides of his pedigree, so he could be expected to improve. Still nobody ever thought he would end up the greatest money-winner in the world but he did. And the way he did it got the crowds. He always carried that high Man o' War head, and when he began his stretch run it came up even higher. Oh, he was something to see. No horse ever came from so far back to win as he did, time and again."

"How I would have loved to see him! Did you go to see him run that day, Louis?"

"I certainly did and I'll never forget it. When he came striding into the paddock before the race there was a sort of gasp from the crowd. He was a 'picture horse' if there ever was one. High-headed with a bronze chestnut coat that shone. He was the handsomest horse I have ever seen. As he stood looking out over the crowd he looked like a king."

42

"He sounds just wonderful, Louis. He won didn't he? I know he won."

"Yes, he won just as he was expected to, but he gave that crowd a thrill they'll remember. This was the first time he had ever raced in New England, and, although most of the people had read of how he came from way back in a terrific stretch run, they weren't prepared for what they saw that day. At the half-mile pole he was not only last, he looked to be thirty lengths back. And this was the great horse they'd heard so much about. You could hear a groan come from the crowd as well as jeers. At the far turn he was about the same, and you could tell that the crowd had given up on him. And then it happened! His head came up even higher and he began his drive. You never saw anything like it. I'd never have believed a horse could close like that. The horses in front seemed to be standing still. It was over long before they reached the finish. With his head high and his mane flying he came over the line all by himself. The crowd went wild. I never heard such cheering as he got when he came back to the winner's circle. People were clapping each other on the back and yelling. They'd seen a great horse and they all knew it."

"Oh Louis I would have loved to have seen that. He must have been wonderful. Weren't you lucky to be there!"

"I was and Stymie brought more luck to me. I was so excited thinking about the race that I didn't even notice the next one. Then I decided to get away before the crowd and skip the last race. It was only a cheap claiming race and after seeing Stymie I wasn't interested in such horses. I was going along past the fence

44

that led to the track just as the field left the paddock and paraded by. Suddenly I saw something that pulled me up short. There was a high-headed chestnut horse with a certain look of pride and fire in his eye. You couldn't miss it. Here was Stymie's look. He was an old campaigner; you could see he had been fired in both front legs, and both hind ankles were taped. He had seen his best days but there was still that proud look. He still had some of the old fire in him. Maybe this was his day. I looked at the mutual board and saw he was forty to one! That should have been enough for me, but I looked him up in my program. He was by a grandson of Man o' War. He got that look from the same blood as Stymie! The next thing I knew I was at the mutual window, and I was betting more than I intended to.

"When the start came it was just like Stymie's. My horse was last although not as far back as Stymie had been. And he did look a lot like Stymie with his high head and a smooth stride. 'It can't happen twice in one day,' I said to myself, but it did. He began rolling and they came back to him. He still had one good race left in him and this was the day. He came under the wire in front by two lengths and I was almost as excited as with Stymie's race. I came away from the payer's window with more cash in my hand than I had ever had before. All in all it was quite a day. One of the best."

"That was wonderful, Louis. I know what you did with the money. You bought that filly you liked so much, didn't you?"

"I did. The very next morning."

"Did she turn out well, Louis? Were you glad you got her?"

45

"She was wonderful and she became a fine brood mare. It was she who gave me Ladybird. If it hadn't been for Stymie you wouldn't have your filly. If you ever see him you should say, 'Thank you.'"

8

As SPRING turned into summer and the grass grew rich and fragrant in the paddocks Ladybird and her filly were very content together. The youngster was growing fast and soon found how delicious the various green things were. As the summer passed she depended less and less on her mother's milk. When Louis began giving her grain in a feed tub of her own she was very proud. The oats tasted so good, and to have the same thing as her mother made her feel grown up. She had grown several inches in height and more in length. Now the legs no longer seemed out of proportion and she moved with an easy grace. The muscles under her dark coat rippled and flowed with every movement. Youthful gaiety was so strong that it overflowed. Even in the midst of grazing her head would suddenly come up and she would be off like a rocket. It was clear that speed and the love of speed were in her blood.

Louis and Joan were leaning on the paddock fence watching the mare and filly grazing. The filly walked over to the mother and nudged her and then nudged again.

"She wants a race around the paddock," said Louis. "I've often watched her. That's her signal. I've never seen a youngester who loved to gallop as much as she does. Here they go!"

Ladybird gave a leap and a buck as if startled and set off at great speed. Faster and faster she went. Clods of earth spurted in the

47

air from her flying feet. Still the filly, running as lightly as a deer, was right beside her, perhaps just a little ahead.

Louis suddenly exclaimed, "Look at that! Ladybird is wide open and the filly is outrunning her. Sometimes mares hold back to make their foals feel proud, but that isn't so here. Ladybird is really trying. That filly can turn it on. And do you see the high head she carries? You know where that came from, don't you?"

"Is that the Man o' War blood, Louis? Oh, I hope it is."

"I think it is," said Louis quietly. "We can't be sure yet but I think it is." Then, almost to himself, "Yes, sir! I believe it's there."

His eyes never left the flying filly. When they finally stopped their wild gallop he turned to Joan.

"Maybe you've got yourself a race horse," he said.

"You mean a race horse like Stymie, Louis!" Joan exclaimed.

Louis smiled. "There are a lot of race horses but not many like Stymie. He was sort of special. But she might be good. She might be real good. It's too early to be sure, but there's something about the way she moves that gets me. It gives me the feeling I've had when I've seen great horses run." He turned to look at Joan. "You wouldn't be disappointed if you had a race horse instead of a jumper?" he asked.

"No, Louis," said Joan. "You know I've changed lately. All I used to think of was horse shows and hunting. Jumpers were everything. But since I've had my filly I am more excited in watching her grow, seeing how she changes. I see Ladybird in her more all the time. It may sound like a crazy dream but do you know what I want most? A stable; not very big, and some mares and foals and paddocks. I'd like to raise beautiful foals and watch them grow."

Louis looked at the eager, glowing face. "That's what I've always wanted, too, but I haven't been lucky. Maybe you will be. If you want something badly enough it can happen."

"Mother laughs at me. She says all I have to do is find a gold mine."

"It would take money," said Louis. "A lot of money. And I haven't seen any gold mines around lately."

He turned as the filly started on another wild dash around the

49

paddock. He watched the way she flew down the far side with reaching stride and high head. Her speed was breath-taking.

"All the gold mines aren't in the ground," he said softly. "There may be some around."

"She's getting to be a big girl now," said Louis one fall day as they watched the filly playing in the paddock. "Have you thought of a name for her? There's no hurry, but a horse learns its name very soon and it's nice to be able to call and see the head come up. Thoroughbreds raised for racing aren't named until they are almost two. That gives the owners a chance to size them up. No one likes to have a horse called The Finest or Unbeatable running last in a race. You can't always tell by looks. One of the best-looking yearlings I've ever seen sold at Saratoga for $50,000 and he never won a race. That same day a plain-looking colt sold for $700. He was named Alsab and he was one of our very greatest. He won so many big stakes that when he retired he had earned something like a half million dollars."

"He must have been a wonderful horse, Louis, but what a strange name. What does it mean?"

"It doesn't mean anything. It's just the first syllables of the owners' names. I think a horse's name should tell something about him. Either how he looks or performs or how he's bred. Now you'd almost know War Admiral and Battleship would be by Man o' War, who was named after our most powerful battleships. Equipoise was so perfectly proportioned and balanced that his name was a natural. And old Exterminator who just ran his fields

off their legs; his owner was either lucky or had second sight. But that's dangerous ground. What if Exterminator had only been able to exterminate himself? It's better to stick to the breeding and try to suggest both the sire and dam if you can. You have Shining Armour and Ladybird. Let's see what you can come up with. If you find a name that suggests the breeding of your filly and has a good ring to it I'll give you an A on your homework."

He smiled into the earnest young eyes. "Try to make it good," he said. "It may be more important than you think."

9

"I THINK I've got it!" cried Joan as she arrived at the stable next morning.

"The name, you mean?" asked Louis. "I hope it isn't anything like Tip Toe Through the Tulips. I knew of a horse once with that name. Imagine that poor horse having to carry all that and a rider too." He smiled at the eager face. "I know it won't be anything silly. What did you decide on?"

"Well, I kept thinking of Shining Armour and his sire, Gallant Knight, and of course Ladybird and all she did. And then how proudly my filly carries her head. I thought maybe Gallant Lady might be a good name for her."

She watched Louis' face anxiously.

"Wonderful!" he said. "Perfect! She won't be a lady for some time but I think it's going to fit her. Can't you hear it come over the loud-speaker, 'The winner, Gallant Lady——!' "

"Oh, Louis, do you really think so? To me she's wonderful, but do you really think she's that good?"

"You can't be sure. Nothing is certain in this game. But when I was around the track I used to gallop the green two-year-olds. They said I had a way with them. One day the trainer asked me which I liked best. It turned out that I was right. I was with him for four years until I got too heavy for an exercise boy, and each spring he asked me to grade the two-year-olds. He saw them from

53

the ground, but I had them under me and that made a difference." Louis looked a little embarrassed. "Maybe I was just lucky at guessing, but that trainer really trusted my judgment. He said I had an eye for a horse."

"Of course, Louis. You are the best. Why shouldn't he come to you?"

Never a day passed through the autumn, that Joan wasn't at the stable as soon as school was out. By now the filly looked forward to her coming. Undoubtedly the carrots or sugar that were always in Joan's pocket were partly responsible; but even after these tidbits were disposed of and the filly's slender muzzle had explored each empty pocket, she still seemed content to stay beside Joan and receive the caresses and compliments from her young owner. Louis, watching them, was sure that his plan had worked out perfectly, at least this time. There could be no doubt of the affection and understanding between these two. If Joan went into the paddock, the filly followed her like a dog. Louis smiled to see how alike they were; long-legged, young and eager. He noticed how much Joan had grown recently. "They're just a couple of teenagers," he said to himself, "just at the same stage of development although one is seven months old and the other fourteen years. They understand each other. This will be a filly that won't take much breaking. Maybe none."

As Joan came in the stable door Louis could hear the shrill whinny of the filly who felt deserted.

"Louis, Girl's paddock is all grazed clean. There isn't anything left there. Couldn't I take her over along the back road? There's such good grass, you can even smell it as you go by. I let Golden Boy graze there when we came back from riding yesterday. He was crazy about it."

"That's a fine idea," said Louis. "Here's a lead shank. Not that you really need it. She would follow you anywhere. So you call her Girl now?"

"That's just her growing name," explained Joan. "Gallant Lady sounds so important and grown up and she's just a girl yet. So I named her Sweet Girl until she's grown enough so Gallant Lady will seem right."

"A good idea," said Louis. "And it certainly fits her now. This way it will be a little like a graduation. You get a diploma when you graduate, she gets her real name. Not a bad idea. Now you tell her she's got something to work for."

Louis watched from the open stable door as the two youngsters went with long swinging strides toward the lane. He noticed how sweeping the filly's stride was, how the hind hoof came down inches ahead of the mark left by the fore. "Never saw it to fail," he said to himself. "When they stride like that they really can gallop."

His gaze went over to Joan. Even from the back every line of her body showed pride and love for the leggy filly walking beside her so contentedly. He remembered her as a child playing with the fox-hound puppies, her small face shining with joy as they crowded around her for attention. It had always been so with her, that intense feeling for animals. Every horse in the stable had its head over the door of its stall the moment she entered. They all wanted her to come to them. And with this filly, he had never

56

seen such response and understanding between a person and an animal.

"That must be it," said Louis to himself. "When you give out that much, you're sure to get something back."

10

Louis looked at the tall slim girl in her neat jodhpurs. He smiled. "The day has come at last. I guess you thought it never would. They grow fast but not fast enough if you count the days and weeks and months as you have been doing. But today you can ride her, your first ride on her. Aren't you excited?"

Joan's face looked troubled. "Louis," she said at last, "I've got to tell you something. I shouldn't have done it, but I just couldn't help it. I've already ridden her."

"You've ridden her!" he said with a surprised look on his face. "When? Where did you ride her?"

"It was only last week," she said looking at Louis pleadingly. "You know you told me she was strong enough to carry me and that you were going to start us today. I was grazing her in that big field back of the lane, and she looked so wonderful and strong I just couldn't resist getting up and sitting on her. She seemed to like to have me up there. It was wonderful!"

"You sat on her!" Louis said, still with that surprised look on his face. "She didn't do anything?"

"No, she just went around the field a few times."

"Walking quietly?" asked Louis.

"Well, she started out that way," said Joan, twisting the toe of her boot in the turf, "but she felt sort of good so she trotted and cantered a little."

Louis shook his head as if stunned. "A Thoroughbred filly, never been ridden, no saddle, no bridle, and you cantered a little!"

"Oh, but she had on her halter and you know she always minds. She stops at my voice. Please don't be angry with me, Louis. We didn't go fast. Just a slow, easy canter."

"A slow, easy canter," Louis repeated softly. "A slow, easy canter." He turned to Joan. "No, I'm not angry. I don't know if

it's courage or just blind faith but I'm proud of you. I'm proud of you both."

Louis and Joan were standing at the fence watching the filly galloping in her paddock. Her smooth, reaching stride was beautiful and rhythmic. Suddenly her head went up and she went into high. Joan was breathless as she watched the flashing speed that seemed incredible.

"I don't see how any horse could run faster, Louis!" exclaimed Joan. "Isn't she absolutely wonderful? And the way she carries her head! Isn't that like Stymie?"

"I was just thinking that," said Louis. "And she has another thing that Stymie and all the Man o' Wars had. Notice how sloping her shoulder is. That makes that high head natural. If she had a straight shoulder she would have to carry a low head or she wouldn't be worth a nickel. Many horsemen used to say that no horse could go a distance if he carried a high head. And here was Stymie who could go as far as horses run, and he carried the highest head of any horse that ever stepped on a track unless it should be Man o' War. And Man o' War and many of his sons and daughters could run horses into the ground at any distance." He turned to her and said earnestly, "Try never to have a prejudice. Just keep your eyes open. That's the way to learn."

He looked at Joan and saw how absorbed she was in what he said. "I am going to tell you something that I want you to remember. Man o' War was only beaten once as a two-year-old, and that was by bad luck. By the time he was three, most of the other

trainers were afraid of him. But there was one who had a big stable and a wealthy owner behind him. He was a proud man who couldn't stand being beaten. Finally he grew to hate the horse. Called him 'that big lobster.' Man o' War was red you know, red chestnut. Here was a horseman, a fine experienced horseman, and because of his pride he never saw that horse for what he was; the greatest we ever had, maybe the greatest that ever lived." Louis looked at Joan. "You see why you should have an open mind?"

When they put a saddle and bridle on the filly she merely looked at Joan as if to be sure she approved. Then she stood quietly and allowed the girth to be tightened. Louis kept it as loose as he thought safe. When Joan was in the saddle, the filly looked back to be sure who it was, then went off with a springy stride. There was a lightness and gaiety to the gait, and Joan looked as if she were riding on air.

"They sure are a team," thought Louis as he watched. "They couldn't be closer if they spoke the same language." He looked after them as the gait rose to long, swinging trot.

"In a way they do," he said to himself. "Yes, they certainly do."

11

THE SNOW was falling thickly outside the stable. Inside all the horses were snug in their box stalls. Altogether there were twelve hunt horses and Ladybird and her filly. The sounds and smells were of a contented stable—a slight stamping and fragrant hay being eaten. A little whickering whinny arose as Joan walked in the door, taken up by one horse, then another and finally the shriller sound of the filly, eager and demanding. Louis came from the tack room.

"Hello," he said, "I thought it was you. Nobody else gets that much of a greeting."

"I'm glad they all like me," said Joan, her face pink with the cold, sharp, outside air. "And did you hear Girl here? She just about came through her stall door."

"She misses you, and she misses your rides together. It's hard to keep a youngster like that cooped up. With frozen ground and ice under the snow, I'd never dare turn her out in the paddock. If she would walk around quietly it would be all right, but with the excitement of all that white and the cold she would explode. Might hurt herself badly. Just look at her! Look at the power in that shoulder and the quarters. She might be quite a handful come spring."

"Not with me, Louis. Never with me. She knows me too well. It isn't that I think I'm such a good rider, it's just that I feel I

64

know her through and through. I could never be nervous with her."

"That's a grand feeling to have, isn't it? That's what I was trying for when I bred her. And how that's going to help next year!"

"How do you mean, Louis?"

"Do you remember that your mother said you'd need a gold

mine if you were ever going to have your dream of a small breeding farm come true? She's right. You'd need a small gold mine for even a small layout!" Turning to the filly he rubbed her nose gently. "Here's your gold mine." He looked at the dark, glowing eye of the filly. "At least I think so. Yes, I really think so."

"What is your plan, Louis? You think we should race her?"

"You're the owner so you must decide. I'll try to tell you what I think our chances are. We had a filly in the racing stable I worked for that was very much like her; no better, maybe not quite as good. She won her first race and then went on to win two stakes. Do you know what she earned from those three races? Over sixty-five thousand dollars! What you could do with even half that. You could have what you want so much. Isn't that worth trying for?"

"Oh, Louis! You don't think she could win anything like that!"

"I may be wrong, but I have a strong feeling that I'm not. I know she hasn't got one of those million-dollar pedigrees but she goes back to the best there is. That may have come through."

He paused a moment and then went on. "If you want to go ahead with this, you have to be her exercise boy. You're light and she knows you. We'll have to get her all tightened up and ready to run when we send her to the track. I know how to do that. When she's ready to run we'll van her to Suffolk Downs. The son of the trainer I worked for has a string of horses there. He's a nice fellow, and I know he'll take her. We'll try her in a maiden race there and if she wins then head for Saratoga and try for one of the big ones. She won't be away from you too long. If she's what I think she is,

66

she'll do her job in a hurry. Then you might have Gallant Lady Farm."

"Gallant Lady Farm! Louis, it all sounds too wonderful to be true. What if she isn't as good as we think she is?"

"Then there's no harm done. You'll have your hunter—and what a hunter! Only the hounds will be able to keep ahead of you."

Christmas had come and gone. Joan had received a beautiful new forward seat saddle. Louis had taken charge and was giving it a vigorous rubbing with saddle soap every day. He knew Joan wanted it to have the rich mahogany color of used leather. The filly's present was a gold-colored blanket with her name in black on one corner.

"Man o' War's colors, Louis," said Joan. "Since Girl has his blood, I thought it would be nice to use those colors."

"They might bring you luck. And we may need some. Maybe I was a little optimistic. I still think she's good, but we may run into some pretty nice fillies at the track. She'll have to be just right. We'll really have to do a job."

"When do you think you will start her, Louis? In the spring?"

"No, we want to give her a chance to mature as much as possible. We might start her in July and then be ready for Saratoga in August. Lots of the big stables wait for the Saratoga meeting to start their top two-year-olds. That makes it tough, but we ought to know by then if she belongs in that class or not."

"But are you sure I can get her in shape, Louis? I'll do just what

67

GALLANT LADY

you say, but I don't know anything about racing. I've never even seen a race except on television."

"This won't be racing. We won't even have her galloping at speed until midsummer. At first it will just be hacking; a lot of walking and trotting and a little easy cantering. That way we'll get her in condition gradually and she'll be hard and fit for faster work. A horse brought along like that isn't as likely to go lame when hard training begins. Remember she's only two and a horse doesn't get it's full development until three or even four."

"She isn't two yet, Louis. Not until April."

"That's right but since she's a Thoroughbred she'll be two tomorrow. All Thoroughbreds have their birthday on January 1 no matter when they were born. That's a rule."

"But why is that, Louis?"

"Well, it's like this. There are races for two-year-olds and for three-year-olds. So any foal born during a certain year is officially the same age as the others of that year even though there may be a six-month difference between them. They can't have races for those one year seven months old and another for those that are one year and eight months. They have to put them together. Of course an early foal will have some advantage over a late one, so many breeders try to have early foals." Louis stopped and smiled. "I remember one fellow I heard about who overreached himself. He had a foal born on December 31. According to the rules he was a year old the next day. Can't you just imagine that little fellow being a two-year-old when he was only a year and a day old? What chance would he ever have at the races?"

"That's so unfair, Louis. What did they do?"

"They hid him away for a few days before they registered him. That's just what I would have done, too. It may not be quite honest but it was the only thing to do to be fair to that little fellow." A smile spread over Louis' face. "Sometimes I wonder what the Thoroughbred officials would have done if they had a yearling that was a day old on their hands."

12

THROUGH the open door came a slim figure bearing a small cake before her. On it were two lighted candles. A clear, light voice with a touch of laughter in it sang, "Happy birthday dear Lady, Happy birthday to you."

"No pastries for her," said Louis. "She's in training."

"This isn't pastry. This is a horse's birthday cake. My own special recipe. Hattie was about to quit when I came out to mess up

her kitchen, but then she got interested and helped me. It's made of carrots and oats and a little sugar frosting for the 'Happy Birthday.' There's nothing there that isn't good for her."

The filly came forward curiously. She could smell the oats and carrots but the two small flickering candles were very strange. She thrust her nose close and then snorted and drew back.

"She blew them out, Louis!" Joan cried. "She blew out her candles. That means she gets her wish. I think it means good luck."

"At least it seems to be good luck for her," said Louis as he watched the filly eagerly eating the little cake. "You ought to set up a bakery shop. You might do all right in Kentucky."

April was softly green with the new grass giving a lovely contour to the rolling fields. The earth was soft under the filly's eager feet. All the world was young and fresh; gaiety and hope were in the very air. Today it did not seem at all impossible that this wonderful filly whose spirit and pride came to Joan through the knees and reins could do all that they hoped or dreamed. She surged and throbbed with power. If Joan had not understood her so well she might have been nervous, for here was a supple strength she had never before known.

They came to a grassy meadow and the filly snorted softly at the mere sight of it. Here was where she could gallop a little, wishful of more speed but always obedient to the quiet voice of her rider—the voice she had known so long that meant kindliness and comfort. It never occurred to her to be disobedient.

Today Joan felt a difference in the filly under her. Power and eagerness pulsed through her body. When they began their canter around the field, the filly shook her head a little at the restraint of the reins. Joan realized that she was begging to run. Louis had remarked that the filly was ready for fast work. On a sudden impulse Joan loosened the rein and leaned forward. The effect was electric. The wind whipped through her hair and tears came into her eyes as the filly flew over the green turf. Never had Joan felt

or even imagined such speed. After two turns of the big field she began to take hold of the reins.

"Easy now, easy Girl. That's enough for today. There will be plenty of this soon." Reluctantly the dark filly slowed her pace. She wanted more. She snorted and pranced with an arched neck as she came down to a trot. Joan stroked her shining neck. "I don't know how fast horses can run, but I'm sure they don't run faster than that. I don't see how they could. You're going to be wonderful!" The filly pranced sideways arching her neck proudly.

Joan kept the filly to an easy trot. "Remember Louis will be looking at us. I don't want him to see you all sweaty, so you behave and go quietly." The lovely dark filly nodded her head and sidestepped daintily, pretending to be nervous about a flashing bird that shot across in front of her. "Oh, you Girl!" said Joan. "I never saw you feel so good. Just save a little of that for the race track. Then maybe—maybe——" The stable loomed ahead.

Louis' quick eye went over the filly. "Looks as if you let her out a little," he said, noting the dried-out coat. "How was it?"

"Maybe I shouldn't have, Louis," said Joan, "but somehow I couldn't help it. She just wanted so much to go and I felt I had to see what it was like. You said she was ready for fast work so I didn't think it would do any harm. You don't mind, do you, Louis?"

"Not at all. If you hadn't let her go when she was so full of herself you wouldn't be human. The hot blood isn't all in the horse; there has to be some in the rider too. No horse is bold enough to get over a big fence if he feels uncertainty in the rider.

74

When you let your filly run she knew you enjoyed it as much as she did. That helps."

"How do you mean, Louis?"

"They say the most important thing in riding is to 'be with your horse.' Without that you can't be a good rider; but it should go even farther if you are to be a real horseman. A close seat is important but closeness between the mind of rider and horse is just as important—maybe even more so."

13

"TODAY we'll try to find out where we stand," said Louis to Joan as he led Gallant Lady out of her stall. "She's as hard and fit as she'll ever be." He looked admiringly at the sleek, dark filly. Her burnished coat revealed muscles that flowed and rippled with every movement. From her high, proud head to her flowing tail she was a picture of what a Thoroughbred should be. Louis studied her intently.

"There's nothing that I would want to change," he said. "When you've looked at horses as long as I have you won't say that very often. There's almost always something." He patted her proudly arched neck. "If she runs to her looks we'll really have a race horse."

For the last month they had been using the half-mile track at the Fair Grounds for the filly's workouts. Some trotters were training there and the track was in good condition. Although Gallant Lady was still covering many miles on the wooded roads and bridle paths, Louis felt that she had reached the point in her training where she needed fast gallops on a racing surface.

"She's been going along at a good pace," said Louis, "but we've never really let her run. Keep a snug hold on her, but let's see what she really has in the way of speed." As they walked up to the start, Louis took a watch from his pocket.

76

When Joan turned the filly, Gallant Lady sensed this was something different. Perhaps the sight of Louis standing, watch in hand, indicated something new and special. Joan felt a surge of power as she leaned forward and they were flying. The green landscape slipped by at an amazing rate. Before she realized it they were around the far turn and surging down toward the finish line. Never had Joan felt such speed! Louis seemed only a blur as they swept past him.

"Easy, Girl, easy," coaxed Joan as she tried to ease up the smooth-striding filly. "Come now, that's enough." But even around the turn the high head and drumming hoofs showed that she had not had enough of this wonderful game. Now Joan knew she had a horse that would never need whip or spur. Everything she had was there for the asking. She was like Golden Boy in her willingness and eagerness. But she had much more. Not in spirit but in speed here was something far beyond the range of that fine horse.

As they approached Louis, Joan could see that he was excited. He was usually so calm but here he was waving his watch over his head. "A half in forty-eight," he cried, "and around two turns. She's ready for the races right now. We ought to send her down to the track soon."

Joan's eyes that had been shining with excitement clouded over. "That's what worries me, Louis. We've never been away from each other, even for a single day. I'll miss her so terribly and worry about her and I think she'll miss me too. We understand each other so well but how will she be with strangers? Won't she be nervous and upset?"

78

"I've thought of that," said Louis soberly. "Many horses are upset by a change. How your filly, who has been so close to you, would take it has been on my mind. I think we'd better change our plans a little."

"And not race her? Oh I do want her to race at least once so that people can see how wonderful she is. It's only that I hate to have her away from me so long."

"I have another idea and maybe a better one," said Louis. "We'll be shooting at the moon but if it comes off it will happen in a hurry."

"That sounds wonderful, Louis. What is it?"

"It will depend on your mother's agreeing, but I'm pretty sure she will. She's almost as proud of the filly as you are."

"I'm sure she'll agree with you on any plan you have, Louis. She's all excited about seeing Gallant Lady race."

"Well, here's my idea. The change from here to the excitement of the track is quite something. It would take most horses quite a while to get used to it. I'm just betting on this filly's intelligence to make the change quickly, but I don't think she can do it unless you are with her all the way."

"Oh that's what I want, Louis. I think she's got to know I'm always nearby."

"So do I," said Louis. "Maybe it's needed both ways," he added, smiling at the earnest young face. "This way you won't be separated. We'll take her down ourselves in my trailer van. You'll be with her all the time she's learning about racing. You can be her exercise boy when she works out in the mornings."

"Would I be allowed to? I thought all the jockeys and riders at the track were men."

"You couldn't ride in a race but you could in morning workouts. Quite a few trainers use a girl now and again, especially for their more sensitive, nervous horses. They say that young horses respond better to a girl's light hands and gentle handling." He looked at her with a smile. "You'll make quite an exercise boy. Wait till they see you."

Joan laughed and flushed a little. "They'll be so busy looking at my filly they won't even see me. Will there be much for her to learn?"

"She's already in fine condition and ready to race. She loves to run, and I think she'll take to the track like a duck to water. All she has to do there is the thing she loves most. I'm not worried about that part of it. The real problem will be the starting gate. It's a pretty strange-looking thing to a horse seeing it the first time, and being locked in those narrow stalls is something a horse has to get used to. But she's smart and with you on her back to give her confidence, we might be all right. If she only comes out of that gate right she might be on the front end all the way. If she does you'll have your Gallant Lady Farm."

"On just one race?"

"On one race. We're shooting high. We're going after the Mademoiselle Stakes. Fifty thousand dollars. Lots of people will think we're crazy. Maybe we are." Louis patted the dark filly's neck and looked at her dark, glowing eye. "But somehow I don't think so. I think Bright Armour outbred himself this time." He

80

patted her again. Almost to himself he said, "I think she goes back to the great one."

"I know I shouldn't count on anything, Louis, but if she should win would you help me about my farm? Couldn't we be partners? You know so much and I couldn't do anything without you."

"I'm getting a little old for hunting," said Louis slowly. "And that's what I've always wanted to do. Maybe we could have a small place with just a few brood mares. But good ones. Like Ladybird and Gallant Lady." His eyes had a faraway look. "Gallant Lady Farm," he said softly. "That would really be something."

14

EARLY morning on the backstretch of the race track presented a fascinating picture to Joan. Louis had called for her and her mother shortly after dawn, but there was no trace of sleepiness in the girl's eyes when she saw all the horses and activity around the stables. Horses were galloping singly or in groups of twos and threes. Every now and then there was a drumming of hoofs that grew in volume as two horses drove by at racing speed. Horses were everywhere, some being walked to cool out. Many an exercise boy glanced appreciatively at the slim girl in sweater and trim boots but Joan had eyes only for the horses. They all looked so sleek and beautiful that her heart sank. Was her filly really good enough to have a chance against horses like these?

Even before they reached the stable they were greeted by a high whinny. Gallant Lady had already seen Joan. The young girl hurried forward and gently caressed the dark head, speaking softly to her all the while.

"How was it, Girl?" she whispered. "Did you mind? Does all this upset you?" The look in the filly's eyes reassured Joan. "Why I believe she likes it!" exclaimed Joan. "Just look at her. She's like a girl going to her first party."

"That's right," spoke a voice behind her. Turning, she met the direct gaze of a lean, tan-faced man. "I'm Don Clark," he said not waiting for Louis' introduction. "And you're my new exercise

82

boy. Between us we've got our work cut out for us. We've got a week to get your filly ready to run against some of the top ones here. We won't even have time to give her a race for experience. If it had been anybody else that suggested it, I would have turned it down without seeing the horse; but I've known Louis too long. I've never known him to be wrong—at least not much wrong," he said with a smile as he laid his hand on Louis' shoulder. "My common sense tells me we haven't got a chance in a thousand, but if Louis says we have then we'll give it everything we've got."

He turned and looked long at Gallant Lady. "She's really got conformation," he said at last. "You can't fault her. And I've never seen nicer manners in any horse. You can see that she's had a lot of care and gentle handling. That all helps, but we've got to see what she'll be like on the track. Suppose you put a saddle on her, Louis, and we'll give her a little gallop. I can see she's in top condition. Tomorrow we'll really open her up and see what she can do."

When Joan was in the saddle, Mr. Clark asked her to jog around once and let the filly look at everything. "She's been working by herself and she'll have to get used to horses around her. Stay away from the rail so you'll be out of the way of the horses galloping."

Joan felt the power under her as they went down the track. The filly went quietly but she seemed like a racing motor that was idling. When horses galloped by she gathered herself and Joan knew it was only the long training in obedience that kept her from taking off after them. Even so she was quivering with eagerness and excitement and it required a little pressure on the reins to remind her that she must obey. When they got back to where the trainer leaned on the outside rail beside Louis and her mother he said, "You've got a handful of horse there. Do you suppose you could gallop her a half without her getting away from you?"

Joan nodded. "I know I couldn't hold her the way she feels now if she didn't mind my voice, but I'm sure I can do it."

"Good girl. Just jog down to the quarter pole over there and then gallop her around to me here. Not wide open; just a good gallop. I want to see her action and how she handles herself."

As they jogged along and came closer and closer to the black and white pole Mr. Clark had indicated, Joan began to have a small doubt in her mind. She felt a surging power beneath her that seemed limitless, and for the first time she began to wonder if she could hold the filly once she was galloping. It almost seemed that Gallant Lady knew what the trainer had said, for as they reached the quarter pole a shiver ran through her. Then there was a thundering of hoofs and two horses drove past them at top speed. Joan let them get well by and down the track before she leaned forward and gave Gallant Lady her head. The filly leaped forward. Joan tried to slow her, but the hot Thoroughbred blood was up. She had her eye on the horses racing in front of her and she was flying. As they hit the top of the stretch, Joan could see that the distance between Gallant Lady and the two in front had been cut to a much smaller margin. All around the turn she was steadily gaining in spite of Joan's efforts to slow her down. After they passed the trainer, Joan gradually felt the filly respond to the

reins. The two in front had evidently finished their workout, for they were being pulled up. Once Gallant Lady was passed them, she came down to a walk and Joan turned her around. As they jogged back she was worried. What would the trainer think of her, especially when she had told him that she could hold her filly to the pace he wanted? She studied his face. Was that a slight smile at the corner of his rather serious mouth?

"That was quite a gallop," he said.

"I know," said Joan. "I'm sorry. I never knew her to be like that. She just had to go after those horses and I couldn't hold her in.

I don't suppose you'll want me to ride her anymore," added Joan miserably.

"It's not that bad," answered Mr. Clark. "You just changed our schedule a little. We had our speed trial today instead of tomorrow."

"Did you like the way she gallops?" asked Joan anxiously. "Is her action all right?"

The trainer smiled. "She'll do. Do you know who that bay horse up ahead of you was? Only the best two-year-old filly on the grounds. And you were cutting them down all the way. They weren't loafing either." He looked at his watch then his eyebrows went up and he looked again.

"She'll do," he said quietly. "Yes, I think she'll do."

15

WHEN Joan arrived at the stable next morning there were two men waiting for her. One of them stepped forward and said, "We're from the *Herald* and I'd like to talk to you for a few minutes. I saw your filly in that workout yesterday and my paper would like a story about her and you. I've talked a little to Don Clark and I see it can make quite a story. Suppose you tell me about it in your own way; how you got the filly and raised and trained her."

"It was really Louis who did everything. I just helped when I could. He bred the filly especially for me——" The deep interest of her listener carried Joan along and soon the whole was told. The man made notes from time to time and once or twice shook his head as if in disbelief.

"A story-book horse," he said under his breath.

"Would you mind posing for a picture?" he added. "You and your horse. I want it to go with my story."

The other man got out a big camera and they went into the stable. "I just want a close-up of the two," he explained to the photographer.

Joan stood beside the stall looking up at her filly with love and admiration in her eyes.

"That's it," said the reporter quickly. "That's just right." A bulb flashed, startling both the filly and Joan.

"Thank you," said the reporter as he shook her hand, "and the best of luck. I'll be rooting for you and so will a lot of people after they read the story. Look for it. I hope you like it."

"The one thing I'm really worried about is the starting gate," said the trainer soberly. "She's never even seen one, let alone been in it. Most horses take time to get used to being closed in a gate and to break fast when the bell rings and the gate opens.

I had one a while ago that never did learn. He hated the gate and fought against it. That killed his chances, for he really had speed and could have been a good one."

He turned to Louis. "The time is so short we can't afford to make any mistakes. We'll try her in the gate today; have it open at both ends and let her walk through a few times. Saddle her up, will you, Louis? She knows you so well it will help give her confidence and she'll need it today. That starting gate is going to look mighty strange to her."

He turned to Joan and said, "Just jog her around once and meet us at the gate. Let her look at everything and keep her as quiet as you can."

Workouts were over and only a few horses were walking around cooling out. Although Joan could feel the power and eagerness in every stride, the filly obeyed voice and rein; but she went as if she had springs in her feet.

As they approached the starting gate, Joan could feel through knees and reins that her horse saw it and was a little upset by that formidable contraption. It looked strange and forbidding even to Joan, but she stroked the filly's dark neck and spoke soothingly. "Now Girl, it's nothing to be afraid of. Just look it over. It won't hurt you."

She urged her closer and closer until they stood beside it. Joan, talking to her quietly, let her stand there, blowing softly through her nostrils. When Louis and the trainer arrived the filly had lost most of her nervousness.

"Good girl," said Mr. Clark. "That's half the battle. Never

try to force a nervous horse or you'll really have trouble on your hands. Slow, easy and gentle is the story. It was Teddy Roosevelt who said, 'Speak softly and carry a big stick.' That may be right for people but with horses it should be, 'Speak softly and carry no stick.'"

Both the front and rear doors of the narrow stalls in the starting gate were open. "See if you can walk her through one of them," said the trainer. "If she objects, let her stand until she makes up her mind. Encourage her but don't force her."

Clearly the filly did not like or trust this strange thing but she was so used to obedience and had so much faith in her rider that with only slight hesitation she entered a stall. Halfway through she gave a hurried leap out of the other end. If this was a trap she wasn't going to be caught.

"Not bad," said Mr. Clark. "Not bad at all for the first time. Try again. I want to get her so that she will walk through quietly."

The second time was better, and after repeating the performance a dozen times Gallant Lady was walking through the stall without a trace of nervousness.

"Now let her stand in the stall for a minute and then walk her out," directed the trainer. Gallant Lady's performance was perfect.

"That's a good first lesson," said the trainer patting the dark filly's shining shoulder. "Good Girl. If we only had time we could make a real nice post horse of her. She has the intelligence and the manners. But there is so much to learn and so little time to learn it in. Tomorrow we have to try her with the gates closed. How she'll take that I don't know but we'll have to find out.

Then the next day you'll break her out of the gate at a gallop," he said, turning to Joan. "Then she'll know what it's for, maybe. The running part is the least of my worries. I've had horses that could really run but wouldn't unless driven to it. She doesn't need any urging. I've seldom seen a horse that loves to run as she does. If she gets out of this gate in a decent start we can stop worrying." He looked at the filly critically. "And maybe start cheering," he added.

"When do you try her out of the gate under racing conditions, bell and all?" asked Louis.

"That's the real trouble. We can't," said the trainer with a worried look. "You know how it can upset a young horse when those doors fly open and the bell starts clanging. Especially the first time. I've seen some that could hardly be got near the gate for a while after that. You have to start all over again. We'll just take a chance that when the gates open she'll go with the others. It's a gamble the way we're playing it but that's what we're doing all the way. An unraced filly out of an unraced mare by a stallion that never won a stake. And we're running against a field that has three stakes winners. According to the book we're not only way out in left field—we're over the fence."

He turned to look at the filly again. "And with all that I think we've got a chance. If she comes out of the gate right we've got a real good chance."

16

DAWN was showing through the curtains in the hotel room. Joan was already awake. With the excitement that filled her days, morning never came too soon. She stretched happily as she recalled the dream from which she has just awakened. She could still see clearly the soft green paddocks and the mares with their little foals snuggling close to their mothers' sides. There had been one that looked just as Girl did when she was small, dashing around the paddock with the same light gaiety and flashing speed. Beyond was a trim white stable. Everything was just as in her daydreams. Strange that she should have dreamed it so exactly, even to the name over the stable door—Gallant Lady Farm. Maybe this meant good luck—the very best of luck. She told herself not to be too hopeful but her heart felt very light.

She heard the morning paper being pushed under the door. Hurrying out of bed she brought it to the window. Turning quickly to the sports page she gave a little gasp. There was a large picture of Gallant Lady and herself. "There is a story-book horse at the Downs, training for the Mademoiselle Stakes," she read.

The facts behind the story read like fiction, and pretty fancy fiction at that. A dark-brown two-year-old filly named Gallant Lady that never saw a race track until three days ago is scheduled to run against five of the best fillies on the grounds, all of them winners and three that are stakes winners. Her

94

exercise boy in the mornings is her owner, a lovely, dark girl of sixteen, who handles her as if the reins were silken threads. The understanding between the two is something that has to be seen to be believed. Still it is not so hard to understand when it is realized that these two have been almost constant companions from the day the filly was born. No one else has ever ridden her. Miss Joan Jamieson broke and trained her, with the advice of the huntsman of the Grafton Hounds, a very experienced horseman. They brought the filly to the track so fit that in her first workout she was sensational, turning in the fastest half mile seen in some time. Don Clark, a seasoned horseman who has the filly in charge, makes no secret of the fact that he thinks the filly has a chance even though so new to the game. If Gallant Lady pulls this off we can go to fairy tales for plots after this.

Joan dropped the paper to her lap. Her eyes were very bright. She went quietly over to the bed and saw that her mother was just stirring. "Look," she said holding up the paper. "It's all about Girl. Everybody will know about her now."

The day of the Mademoiselle Stakes was bright and sunny. The track was fast and conditions were ideal for the big race. Joan, her mother and Louis came out to the track early to see Gallant Lady in a short gallop under the jockey who was to ride her in the race. Joan's worry of how the filly would take to a stranger riding her was soon dispelled when she saw how he stroked Gallant Lady's neck and spoke soothingly to her. His hands were light on the reins and the filly went very easily and willingly.

"He's the best boy with young horses that I know of," said the trainer to Joan. "He has light hands and a way with horses. They run for him. Seldom uses a whip; today he won't even carry one. That's something your filly doesn't need. She puts out everything when you ask for it." He turned and looked seriously into Joan's face.

"I don't want you to be too disappointed," he said. "Your filly may not win today. Never having broken from a gate in a race,

you can't tell how that will be. But there's one thing I can promise you. Sometime during the race she's going to do some real running. Something they'll remember. If she gets off to a bad start it won't be enough. But whatever happens you're going to be proud of her. Will that be enough?"

"Yes, oh yes," said Joan in a strained voice. "And thank you so much for everything."

When the bugle blew and the horses paraded onto the track, Joan felt her breath come quickly. Her eyes searched eagerly until she saw Gallant Lady. How lovely she looked with the sun giving a burnished sheen to her dark coat, her head carried so high and proudly. Now Joan knew that her name really fitted. There was something about her that was more than pride. In her eye, in her every move there was a feeling of courage and determination. Somehow it came through that here was a horse that would always do her best, never hold anything back. Perhaps the crowd felt it too for there was a ripple of applause as she went by.

"Gallant Lady," was heard from many sides. "That's Gallant Lady." Evidently many people had read about her filly and Joan felt a thrill of happiness. Now they would see how wonderful she really was. Then she noticed the jockey's silks. She knew Gallant Lady was racing in Mr. Clark's colors since she had none of her own, but she had not known what they were. A thrill ran through her. Black and gold! Man o' War's colors! Surely this was a good omen.

The start was across the track at the top of the backstretch so

it was hard to see what went on. Mr. Clark offered Joan his glasses, but she knew her hands were shaking too much to be able to use them. Here it was at last! Everything that the race had meant before was blotted out by the one hope that Gallant Lady would do well so that this huge crowd could see how wonderful she really was.

At last all the horses were in position and the stall gates were closed. As the starter waited for them to quiet down, Joan felt as if her heart had stopped. Then it raced on as she heard a shrill bell and the cry: "They're off!"

At first she could make out nothing clearly for her eyes seemed misted over. Then she saw a cluster of horses flying down the backstretch and one lone straggler, far behind. As her eyes cleared she saw that the last horse carried the black and gold silks! So it had happened. Her filly's inexperience at the gate had cost her all chance in the race.

"Too bad!" exclaimed the trainer in her ear. "She must have been backing up when the start came. She's going beautifully but it's too late now. She can never spot those horses ten lengths. If she'd broken well, she'd really have made a race of it."

Joan fumbled for a handkerchief and turned away to wipe her eyes. She couldn't bear to see her horse trying so hard and everything so hopeless.

Suddenly a new sound came over the roar of the crowd. "Gallant Lady!" Someone's voice rose to a scream. "Look at her come!"

Other voices joined in until it became a wild chant. "Come on,

99

you Gallant Lady. Come on!" Trembling with excitement Joan turned and saw with unbelieving eyes that the dark filly carrying the black and gold was coming like a ship under full sail. As they hit the far turn she was within a length of the field, still closely clustered. Around the turn she went to the outside, swept up to the last horse, then went by.

When they swung into the stretch it was hard to see what was happening but the announcer's voice came to the rescue. "In the stretch it's Brown Jade by a length, Blue Sparkler by a half and Gallant Lady," came booming over the loud-speaker. "At the eighth pole it's Brown Jade by a half, Blue Sparkler by a neck and Gallant Lady coming very fast."

Now they were close enough so Joan could see them clearly. "Come on, Girl!" she cried and her heart raced as she saw that proud head come up even higher as she drove forward in a last surge of speed.

"She's going to make it!" Louis' voice rose in a frenzy of excitement. "It isn't possible but she's going to do it!"

The finish line was only yards away and the bay and brown were head and head. With a last lifting drive, the brown head showed in front as they flashed over the finish line.

"Gallant Lady!" came a roar from the crowd. "Gallant Lady wins!"

The trainer helped Joan push through to the winner's circle. They got there just as the dark filly, her coat shining with sweat, was led in. As Joan looked at that proud head she knew what she had. Here were honesty and courage past belief. When the filly came over to nuzzle her, Joan threw her arms around her neck and her eyes filled with tears.

"Oh Girl!" she said. "You gallant Gallant Lady!"

17

TIIE FENCES were of beautifully fitted post and rail; the stable glowed white against towering trees. Grass in the paddocks was green and lush. It looked the dream of perfection to Joan's eager eyes.

"Oh no!" she exclaimed. "We could never have this."

"We have it," said Louis quietly, "if you like it and want it. The man who owned it was mad about horses. All sorts of horses; trotters and gaited and some Arabians. Nothing was too good for them. Wait till you see the inside of the stable. It's really something. When he died he told his wife never to sell to anyone but a horseman. She has held with that idea even though she has had some good offers. When I spoke of you she already knew all about you and said you could have the place. And at a reasonable price. She's a very nice woman and she wants to meet you. Come along."

When they came to the house set deep among the trees and shrubbery they saw a grey-haired lady at work among the flowers. She straightened up when she saw them approaching, and Joan was at once aware of her dark, piercing eyes.

"So this is the young lady that upset them all at Suffolk Downs. She and her lovely mare. I've seen you on the roads, my dear, and I think your Gallant Lady is one of the nicest horses I ever saw. My husband would have been proud to have her in his

stable, I know. Now come and look at the stable and see if it suits you."

The spacious stable was beautiful from the outside but the interior surpassed all Joan's expectations. The box stalls were large and beautifully finished and all the fittings were brass which shone against the dark wood of the stalls. There were twelve stalls in all—more than enough for Joan's and Louis' modest plans, even looking far ahead. Joan was delighted with everything, and the bargain was quickly sealed with a firm hand shake from Mrs. Aldrich.

"May I give you a little advice?" asked Mrs. Aldrich. "Running even a small farm takes money—a lot of money. Keep your mare fit. She may have to go to the races again. *You're* lucky. When you need money you don't need a bank. And when she's all through racing, what a brood mare she will be! She will make your farm."

As they rolled down the drive, Joan looked again at the lovely, green paddocks. Already she could see the young foals at play. Louis looked over at her with his quiet smile.

"So we really have it. Gallant Lady Farm. She'll love it here. It's her farm."